THE CUTTING EDGE

SO-AJE-216

Huntington Public Library
7 East Main St.
Huntington, MA 01050

Art   Jeff Anderson

Story   Terry Murray

Lettering   Steve Harrison

Series concept   Edward Chatelier

LION

SO MANY VOICES.

IF ONLY I COULD SEE THEIR FACES.

MY PEOPLE, WE MUST BE UNITED IF WE ARE TO DEFEAT THE ARMY OF NAYTHEN SKRITHE.

WE'RE NOT YOUR PEOPLE.

IT'S YOUR FAULT WE'VE BEEN INVADED.

THE FICKLENESS OF HUMANS NEVER CEASES TO AMAZE ME.

COLLECTING ROCKS, FRIEND?

A PRESENT FOR OUR PRECIOUS QUEEN.

YOU WOULD STONE HER?

THAT'S BETTER THAN SHE DESERVES.

WANG SHUH WAS RIGHT.

THE GIRL AND HER PRIEST HAVE BROUGHT US NOTHING BUT TROUBLE.

MEN ARE SUCH FOOLS.

WOULD YOU HAVE WEPT LONG FOR ME, MY LOVE?

BUT DARLING, I KNEW YOU WOULD WIN.

IT WAS INEVITABLE I WOULD MAKE ENEMIES.

YOU KILLED MY SON! YOU SHE-DEMON. YOU WITCH. I'M GOING TO HAVE YOU DROWNED FOR WHAT YOU'VE DONE.

BUT THEY WERE NEVER AS POWERFUL AS MY FRIENDS.

I WOULD NEVER HAVE BELIEVED IT POSSIBLE.

MY DAUGHTER HAS THE HIGH MERCHANT HIMSELF EATING OUT OF HER HAND.

OUR DAUGHTER, HUSBAND.

AND SHE HAS STILL TO OBTAIN FOR US HIS PRIME CONTRACTS.

MY PARENTS WERE BECOMING A LIABILITY.

THEY'RE NOTHING BUT SECOND-RATERS.

MY TALENTS ARE WASTED HERE.

I PLANNED TO BE RID OF THEM.

YOU KNOW I WOULD DO ANYTHING FOR YOU, MY DEAR.

THEN PLEASE, AMYDON, HELP ME BREAK FREE OF MY PARENTS.

EACH DAY HE FALLS FURTHER UNDER HER SPELL.

BUT I WAS NOT THE ONLY ONE WITH PLANS.

IN MY MOMENT OF TRIUMPH I GREW CARELESS. I UNDERESTIMATED MY ENEMIES.

I HAD NOT REALIZED HOW BADLY THEY TREAT YOU.

I WAS AFRAID TO TELL YOU, IN CASE THEY BEAT ME.

WE MUST ACT TONIGHT IF AMYDON IS TO BE SAVED.

I HAD NEVER SET MUCH STORE BY GODS.

I HAD NEVER NEEDED THEM.

HELP ME!

PLEASE, SOMEBODY HELP ME!

NOW, FOR THE FIRST TIME, I PRAYED.

HELP...

I DIDN'T KNOW WHO I WAS PRAYING TO...

... BUT MY PRAYER WAS ANSWERED.

DO NOT BE AFRAID, CHILD.

YOU ARE SAFE NOW.

THE DAY DAARE PULLED ME FROM THE WATER WAS THE DAY CHARISSE DIED.

AND SHEELA COULPE WAS BORN.

TRUE FATHER, YOU HAVE ANSWERED MY PRAYERS.

PLEASE HELP ME PROTECT AND CARE FOR THE ONE YOU HAVE GIVEN ME.

IF ONLY IT WERE THAT SIMPLE.

I MAY HAVE CHANGED MY NAME, AND I MAY ONLY WISH TO DO GOOD NOW...

... BUT IN REALITY I AM STILL CHARISSE.

I CAN NEVER BE YOUR DISCIPLE.

NOT AFTER WHAT I HAVE DONE.

I DESERVE TO BE PUNISHED.

YET DARE I, WHO HAVE BEEN SO WICKED, ASK FOR FORGIVENESS?

I AM TRULY SORRY.

I HAVE COME TO SEE THE QUEEN, BOY.

SIR, SHE IS NOT TO BE DISTURBED.

SHE WILL SEE ME.

I HAVE COME TO SAVE HER.

OPEN UP, YOUR MAJESTY.

YOUR ONE TRUE FRIEND, WANG SHUH, IS HERE TO RESCUE YOU.

WHY, SHEELA, YOU LOOK LOVELIER THAN EVER.

THIS DOES NOT SOUND LIKE THE PRIEST OF VEMON ATROPOS.

YOU MISUNDERSTOOD, MY DEAR. MY ARGUMENT WAS WITH DAARE LEMANDE.

I WISH US TO BE FRIENDS.

I ADMIT I NEED FRIENDS AT THIS TIME.

IT IS BUT A SIMPLE MATTER FOR THE DRAGON GOD TO BE SUMMONED.

SUCH POWER WILL SILENCE YOUR ENEMIES.

AND IN RETURN?

SHARE THE THRONE WITH ME, SHEELA.

WE WOULD MAKE A MAGNIFICENT KING AND QUEEN.

SURELY YOU KNOW OF MY PAST, THAT I AM CHARISSE.

WHICH ONLY ADDS TO YOUR ATTRACTION.

YOU MAY BE BLIND, BUT I LOOK FORWARD TO...

I FEAR YOU ARE DOUBLY MISTAKEN, WANG SHUH.

YOU MAKE MY FLESH CREEP.

AND ?

I AM **NO LONGER** BLIND.

AARGHH!!

I THINK IT'S TIME WE GOT A FEW THINGS STRAIGHT.

YOU THINK ME CORRUPT.

BUT DO YOU DESERVE ANY BETTER FOR A QUEEN?

YOUR SO-CALLED KINGDOM HAS PROSTITUTED ITSELF FOR YEARS.

THE YOLK'S ON YOU, YOUR MAJESTY.

HAW... HAW...

THEY DON'T WANT TO LISTEN.

IN THEIR FEAR, THEY WOULD RATHER MOCK AND RIDICULE ME.

THEY ARE AS CERTAIN OF THEIR FATE AS...

... THE FATE OF THIS EGG.

THEY DO NOT KNOW YOU, TRUE FATHER.

BUT THEY NEED YOU, TOO.

PEOPLE OF BERBEROUS, YOU KNOW AND FEAR ME.

THAT IS AS IT SHOULD BE.

YOU HATE ME FOR DEMANDING YOUR CHILDREN AS SACRIFICES TO MY GOD.

I WARN YOU, WANG SHUH.

BUT IN RETURN HE WILL GRANT YOU HIS PROTECTION.

CAN THIS GIRL MATCH THE POWER OF VEMON ATROPOS?

BE GONE, WANG SHUH, WE WANT NOTHING OF YOUR FALSE GOD HERE.

THERE ARE NO SUCH THINGS AS DRAGONS.

LIGHT WILL TRIUMPH OVER DARKNESS.

NOW WE ARE QUITS, CHARISSE.

I WAS FOOLISH TO UNDERESTIMATE YOU.

BUT YOURS IS THE GREATER MISTAKE.

EIEEAGH!

WELL, MADLIN, NO JOB'S EVER BEEN TOO BIG OR DIFFICULT FOR YOU BEFORE.

BUT WHAT CAN I DO AGAINST THAT?

AIIEEEAH!

AARGH!

RUN FOR YOUR LIVES.

OF COURSE, I SEE NOTHING BECAUSE THERE IS NOTHING TO SEE.

THE DRAGON IS AN ILLUSION.

THE SIGHT GIVEN ME BY THE TRUE FATHER SEES THROUGH YOUR LIES, WANG SHUH.

MY PEOPLE, THIS IS NOT REAL.

WATCH, I SHALL DESTROY THIS PHANTASM.

IT DIDN'T WORK!

THEY STILL SEE THE BEAST.

I'M AS POWERLESS AS I WAS BEFORE.

I MUST GET OUT OF HERE.

HA HA HA

NO! WHAT AM I RUNNING FROM?

SUCH FEAR.

I HAVEN'T HAD SO MUCH FUN IN YEARS.

I HAVE FACED MY MONSTER, WANG SHUH, AND BY THE GRACE OF THE TRUE FATHER I HAVE CONQUERED IT.

WHAAA?

YOU AGAIN?

YOU TORTURE THESE PEOPLE WITH THEIR WORST NIGHTMARES.

NIGHTMARES OF THEIR OWN MAKING.

A WASTED JOURNEY.

WORSE THAN WASTED.

I HAVE FAILED YOU, SHEELA.

HOW THE MIGHTY HAVE FALLEN.

TRUE FATHER, YOU GAVE THEM SO MUCH.

YET THEY WANTED MORE.

IN THEIR GREED THEY SOUGHT TO EXPAND THEIR MINDS.

INSTEAD, THEY HAVE LOST TH

CRACK!

DAARE LEMANDE?

WHAA?

WHO ADDRESSES ME?

YOU ARE TO COME WITH US.

CARELESS, CARELESS AND STUPID, LETTING THEM TAKE ME BY SURPRISE.

BUT I AM THIRSTY FOR BLOOD.

WE SHALL ENTER THEIR TRAP.

IT WILL MAKE THEIR DEFEAT THE MORE HUMILIATING.

PREPARE FOR BATTLE.

WE MARCH ON THE TOWN WITHIN THE HOUR.

WHILE YOU WATCH MY TOKEN FORCE ENTER THE MAIN GATE, WE SHALL TAKE YOU FROM BEHIND, YOU FOOLS.

THERE MUST BE NO WARNING OF OUR APPROACH.

IF YOU SEE ANYONE... KILL THEM.

EXCEPT THE QUEEN.

THAT PLEASURE MUST BE MINE.

EXCELLENT. THEY HAVE ENTERED THE CITY EXACTLY AS I EXPECTED.

PRAISE YOU, TRUE FATHER, FOR SHOWING ME WHERE THE ATTACK WOULD COME FROM.

PLEASE GIVE US COURAGE AND STRENGTH.

NOT A BAD LITTLE TALENT THE GIRL'S GOT.

WE'RE SURE GONNA NEED IT.

IT'S GIVEN US AN EDGE ON NAYTHEN'S WAR HAWKS.

WHO'S NEXT?

SKRITHE?

I AM INVINCIBLE.

UURGH!

SO, THERE YOU ARE, MY TORMENTOR!

I HAVE BEEN LOOKING FORWARD TO THIS MOMENT.

NOW IS THE TIME TO CUT MY LOSSES AND RUN.

WRONG DIRECTION, MADLIN.

NOT SO FAST, SKRITHE.

MADLIN...

WHAT HAVE WE HERE?

I'VE BEEN PAID TO PROTECT THE LADY

AND I INTEND TO.

THEN YOU MUST HAVE A PRICE.

I CAN MEET IT A THOUSAND TIMES OVER.

PERHAPS.

YOU KNOW MY REPUTATION AS A WARRIOR.

YOU DON'T REALLY WANT TO FIGHT ME.

WHERE IS THE PROFIT IN PROTECTING THIS WORTHLESS TROLLOP?

IS THIS NOTHING MORE THAN ANOTHER JOB TO YOU?

I SHALL NOT BE DENIED MY VENGEANCE.

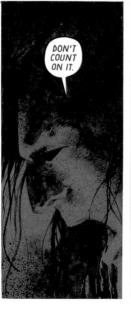

AND YOU CAN NEVER DEFEAT MY ULTIMATE PROTECTOR - THE TRUE FATHER.

A WEAKLING'S DEITY.

MINE ARE THE GODS OF THE STRONG.

YOUR GODS?

DEATH AND DESTRUCTION.

THE TRUE FATHER HAS VICTORY OVER BOTH OF THESE.

THEN LET HIM SAVE YOU!

YAAH! CURSE YOU, GIRL, NO ONE CAN REACT THAT FAST.

I TRIED TO WARN YOU.

I DIDN'T WANT HIM TO DIE, MADLIN. I TRIED TO SAVE HIM.

I'M SURE YOUR TRUE FATHER KNOWS THAT. ME, I'D HAPPILY HAVE SENT HIM TO HIS DOOM.

YOU KNOW, YOU'VE MADE ME LOOK PRETTY FEEBLE.

HE COULDN'T TOUCH YOU.

OH MADLIN, I'M SORRY, I SHOULD SEE TO YOUR WOUND.

HE NEARLY KILLED ME.

IT'LL KEEP.

IT LOOKS, OUCH! AND FEELS WORSE THAN IT IS.

IF YOU SAY SO.

BUT HOW IS THE BATTLE GOING?

NOT WELL. WITH SKRITHE DEAD THE WAR HAWKS SHOULD GIVE UP. BUT THEY WON'T.

WE'RE STILL IN BIG TROUBLE.

LOOK! OVER THERE.

WHO ARE THEY, MADLIN?

OUR RESCUERS, I'D SAY, GOING BY THE WAY THEY'RE LAYING INTO THE WAR HAWKS.

AND MIGHTY GLAD I AM TO SEE...

RAARGH!

ORCS!

WHAT FOUL JOKE IS THIS?

I'LL HAVE NO TRUCK WITH SUCH MONSTERS.

THE ONLY GOOD ORC IS A DEAD ORC.

AND I AIM TO MAKE A LOT OF GOOD ORCS.

TAKE CARE WHERE YOU POINT THAT BOW, MY FRIEND.

LEMANDE!

YOU LEFT TO FETCH THAT?

IN TRUTH, NO.

IT WAS HEDON AND HIS PEOPLE WHO SOUGHT ME.

THEY WISH TO MAKE AMENDS FOR THE PAST.

DO NOT JUDGE THEM BY THE ACTIONS OF THEIR ANCESTORS, MADLIN.

THEY HAVE RISKED MUCH FOR US.

FORGIVE ME FOR LEAVING YOU, SHEELA.

BUT OTHERWISE YOU COULD NOT BE HEALED.

I UNDERSTAND, DAARE, MY DEAR FRIEND.

HOW GLAD I AM TO SEE THE MAN WHO HAS SHOWN ME SUCH LOVE.

MAY I SAY, YOUR MAJESTY, IT IS AN HONOUR TO SERVE SUCH A BEAUTIFUL AND NOBLE QUEEN.

I DO NOT BELIEVE THIS IS HAPPENING.

SINCE WHEN DID WE HAVE ANYTHING TO THANK ORCS FOR?

MADLIN! WE PROBABLY OWE THIS MAN OUR LIVES.

IT'S NO MAN.

AND JUST BECAUSE IT POSSI. MAY HAVE SAVED US, THAT DC MEAN I HAVE TO TRUST IT.

With special thanks to Donald Banks

Text copyright © 1992 Terry Murray
Illustrations copyright © 1992 Jeff Anderson
This edition copyright © 1992 Lion Publishing

Published by
Lion Publishing plc
Sandy Lane West, Oxford, England
ISBN 0 7459 2370 4
Lion Publishing
1705 Hubbard Avenue, Batavia, Illinois 60510, USA
ISBN 0 7459 2370 4
Albatross Books Pty Ltd
PO Box 320, Sutherland, NSW 2232, Australia
ISBN 0 7324 0607 2

First edition 1993

All rights reserved

A catalogue record for this book is available
from the British Library

Library of Congress CIP Data applied for

Printed and bound in Singapore

Huntington Public Library
7 East Main St.
Huntington, MA 01050